TSR2

AN
AEROGUIDE SPECIAL
BY
ANTHONY THORNBOROUGH

AD HOC PUBLICATIONS

INTRODUCTION

ON SUNDAY 27 SEPTEMBER 1964 the skies above Boscombe Down in Wiltshire echoed with the roar of two Olympus engines as a graceful, white aircraft—carrying with it not merely two crewmen but also the hopes, expectations and ambitions of both the Royal Air Force and the British aerospace industry—was put through the tentative paces of its initial test flight. Apart from some minor criticisms, and despite the aircraft having known shortcomings in respect of engine vibration and undercarriage retraction, after they had landed the crew reported that all had gone very well indeed. On 22 February the following year, with almost all the technical problems ironed out and with some 5½ hours of flying time behind it, the aircraft was flown to Warton Aerodrome in Lancashire, spending a few minutes en route at supersonic flight for good measure.

Six months later the project was officially cancelled, the reason cited being its unacceptably high cost. Had the matter rested there, the saga of the TSR.2 might well have faded into history along with the ghosts of the multitude of other technically brilliant postwar aircraft that had the misfortune to incur governmental displeasure, but it did not. In an un-exampled act of official malevolence, the reasons for which to this day continue to escape all clear-thinking individuals, the British Government decreed that all trace of the project—prototypes, jigs, manuals, records—be eradicated.

Thus the fascination with TSR.2 continues—and it will continue on. Incredibly, forty years after the order to cancel, there is reluctance in some official circles even to admit to the existence of the project, and attempts to glean information about it are still met with shrugs and anxious glances

Right: Only two TSR.2s were completed, and XR219 was the only aircraft to fly. It is seen here on a test flight from Warton Aerodrome, March 1965.

Main image: Death: TSR.2 components in the process of destruction at BAC's Salmesbury facility.

over the shoulder. Several of the advisors and contributors to this book (some of whom were intimately concerned with the project), while very willingly giving of their time and knowledge, have asked not to be identified by name.

Conspiracy theorists will draw their own conclusions as to the relevance of the TSR.2 project to the political world of today. In the fullness of time the true and complete story will no doubt be revealed. Or, on the other hand, perhaps it will not . . . **R.D.C.**

THE 'CANBERRA REPLACEMENT'

SIR GEORGE EDWARDS, later Chairman and Managing Director of the British Aircraft Corporation (BAC) and the man put in charge of the TSR.2 project, frequently commented that the placing by the British Government of a military aircraft contract was merely the necessary prelude to their cancelling it—what he described as 'turning taps on just in order to turn them off again'. Such was the uncertain world into which General Operational Requirement GOR.339, which eventually led to the Tactical Strike & Reconnaissance (TSR.2) project, was born, the intent behind which was to give the Royal Air Force another world-beating design to replace its Canberra bomber—equally revolutionary at the time of its introduction to service—and reconnaissance fleet. All this had come amidst Conservative Defence Minister Duncan Sandys' White Paper of 1957, which suggested that manned aircraft were obsolete and that the Defence of the Realm be fulfilled primarily by a nuclear-armed rocket force. Incidentally, the numeric component of the TSR.2's designation was, reputedly, indicative of its envisaged Mach 2+ top speed and proved somewhat ironic given that the great white steed never was given the opportunity fully to be wrung out with its throttles to the firewall, although it was, in every other respect, a supersonic strike aircraft of the very first order and certainly did attain faster-than-sound flight, with more power in reserve.

The British Aircraft Corporation itself was a merger formed in February 1960, welded by the TSR.2 project and fusing together several formerly independent British manufacturers, notably Vickers-Armstrong and English Electric—though some have commented that the TSR.2 was the wrong project to provide the flux for seamless integration. In response to GOR.339 Vickers-Armstrong, with George Henson leading the design team, offered an efficient, svelte twin-engined jet design built around sophisticated 'blind'

The English Electric Canberra (left), the aircraft for which GOR.339 was proposed as a replacement. In the event, the 'Cranberry' would continue inexorably onwards in Royal Air Force service—albeit latterly not in its original bomber role—and celebrated half a century in the front line in 2001. This particular photograph shows a T Mk 4, its yellow trainer bands prominent.

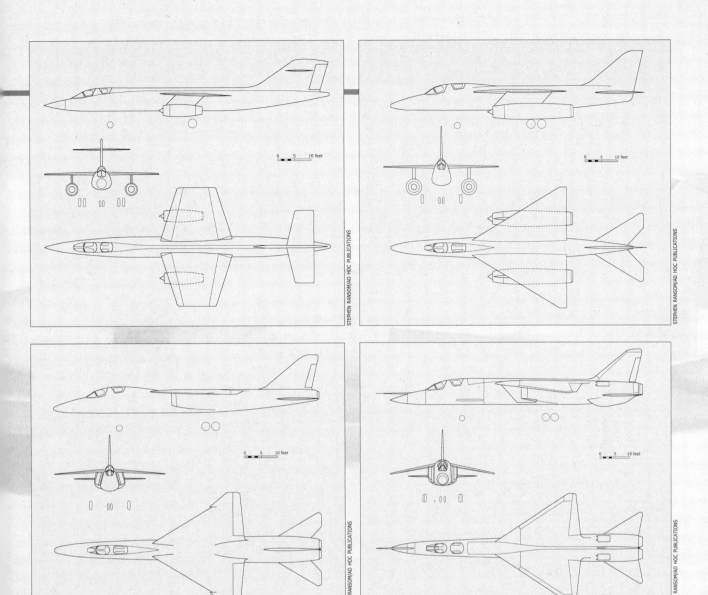

STEPHEN RANSOM/AD HOC PUBLICATIONS

In 1956 English Electric began in-house studies for a prospective replacement for the Canberra bomber, itself a product of the Warton facility. The progression of the project's design sketches (above) shows a series of quite startling changes. The original ideas, designated P.17, showed podded engines in the January 1956 (top left) and January 1957 (top right) layouts; these had been discarded in favour of fuselage-mounted powerplants in the P.17A of October 1957 (above left) and January 1958 (above right). GOR.339 was officially issued in March 1957.

terrain-following navigation and attack systems and known as the Type 571; English Electric's contender, drawn up under Freddie Page's Warton-based design team, was a sleek, delta-winged, twin-seater designated P.17A, and also to be powered by two Rolls-Royce Medway RB.142/3 augmented turbofans. Unlike the Type 571, however, which was conceived as a complete weapons system, the P.17A was all surge and thrust, any avionics being considered as 'add ons' to suit operational requirements.

The RAF and the Ministry concluded that both projects had considerable merit, and so on 1 January 1959 the Government awarded a joint contract

GOR.339 MAIN FEATURES

1 Flight at 1,000 feet, or less, above sea level
2 A radius of action of 1,000nm (including 200nm at low level)
3 A speed of not less than M0.95 at sea level
4 Operation from dispersed sites
5 A ferry range of 2,000nm
6 Ability to carry nuclear weapons or four 1,000lb bombs
7 An automatic flight control system (including automatic landing)
8 Maximum crew comfort at low level
9 In-service date 1964

to Vickers-Armstrong and English Electric to meet GOR.339, and also to Bristol-Siddeley for their uprated Olympus engines. GOR.339 was further refined into RAF Air Staff Operational Requirement 343 (also known as Ministry of Aviation Specification RB.192D) which essentially finalised the design of TSR.2 during 1960.

The designing and construction of such a high-performance weapons system at numerous locations—and in the days of the slide rule, pencil and pad, a quarter of a century before networked systems connected the industry—presented an enormous challenge. Compounding the problems was a complex Ministerial controlling committee system instigated by Sir Solly Zuckerman, a zoologist by trade who had become the chief scientific advisor to the Defence Staff. His system involved a multitude of steering and overseeing committees, and these had an unfortunate tendency to slow down decision-making. Equipment also was classed in one of three categories, *viz.* (a) items purchased by the Ministry and supplied to BAC for TSR.2; (b) equipment purchased by the manufacturers but subject to approval by the Ministry; and (c) items which could be purchased directly provided they met certain criteria such as cost or an arbitrarily prescribed specification. This took away some of the vitally needed project control from the engineers, resulting in delays and cost overruns. However, as it transpired, a good portion of these overruns was ascribable to the inherent complexity of the project. Ultimately, these problems caused much agitation in the Treasury.

The project had many enemies. Lord Mountbatten, at the time Chief of the Defence Staff, was firmly committed to the view that the Senior Service should reassume the strategic role, employing Polaris missiles on submarines, and was particularly fond of the suggestion that the RAF buy into the Navy's Blackburn NA.39 Buccaneer strike jet programme, as this would further reduce Royal Navy unit acquisition costs. A contemporary newspaper article reported that Mountbatten had had calling cards printed showing the Buccaneer and the TSR.2. At meetings he would lay them down, saying, 'You can have five of these [Buccaneers] for the price of one of these [TSR.2]'. Immensely influential, Mountbatten scuppered any hope of an Australian purchase of TSR.2 by convincing the RAAF Air Staff that the aircraft would never be built. Their considerable enthusiasm for TSR.2

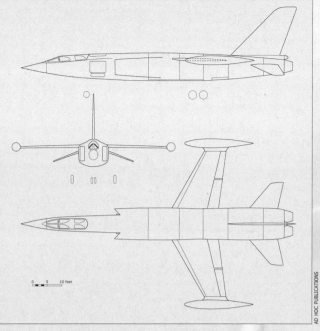

The Supermarine division of Vickers-Armstrong were also developing designs to fulfil GOR.339, one single-engined and another twin-engined and both designated Type 571. The latter—somewhat radical in appearance, as indicated in the drawing above—was proceeded with in the sense that its fuselage formed the basis of the final TSR.2 concept.

The new Royal Navy strike bomber of the time was the Blackburn Buccaneer (below), in 1959 undergoing flight testing. Mountbatten pushed hard for the adoption of this considerably cheaper (but much less capable) aircraft. Ironically, he eventually got his way: the aircraft entered service with the RAF in 1969. Both the Buccaneer and TSR.2 were nuclear bombers, and as such finished in the all-white scheme then standard for aircraft dedicated to that role.

OR.343 MAIN FEATURES

1 Two engines
2 A radius of action of 1,000nm (including 200nm at low level)
3 A speed of not less than M0.9 at sea level and M2 at tropopause
4 A ferry range of 2,500nm
5 Normal take-off/landing distance of 1,300 yards at sea level and ISA +30°C and for dispersed operations 1,000 yards for a 1,000nm sortie and 600 yards for a 450nm sortie
6 Ability to carry one or two nuclear weapons or six 1,000lb bombs
7 A terrain-following capability at 200 feet
9 In-service date December 1965

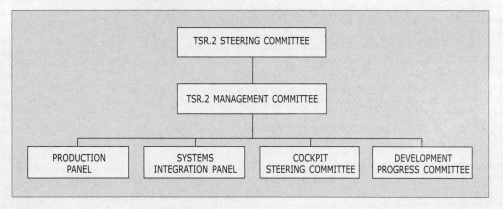

TSR.2 STEERING COMMITTEE			
TSR.2 MANAGEMENT COMMITTEE			
PRODUCTION PANEL	SYSTEMS INTEGRATION PANEL	COCKPIT STEERING COMMITTEE	DEVELOPMENT PROGRESS COMMITTEE

Strangled by red tape: instead of issuing a specification and allowing industry to get on with the job of producing an aircraft in response, the British Government, in the shape of the Ministry of Aviation, set up a plethora of committees to 'oversee' the TSR.2 (right). Political interference was particularly meddlesome in the area of aircraft equipment, and the resultant avalanche of directives and demands for modifications badly hindered the manufacturers' task.

In mid-1958 Vickers formally entered into partnership with English Electric, and the pooling of the two companies' resources resulted in the finalised Type 571—seen here (below) in a July 1959 general-arrangement drawing.

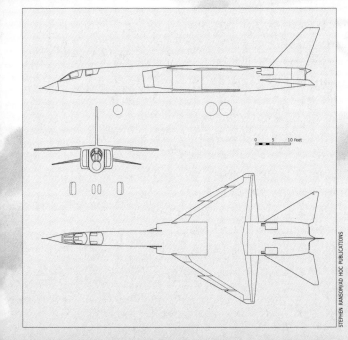

0   5   10 feet

STEPHEN RANSOM/AD HOC PUBLICATIONS

LM
ROYAL NAVY

AD HOC PUBLICATIONS

blunted, the Australians, not surprisingly, turned instead to the United States.

The new Labour Party administration under Harold Wilson, voted into power in 1964, had been anti-TSR.2 whilst in opposition and were determined to cancel all British military aircraft projects and buy from America; even the Concorde supersonic transport was to get the 'chop', but a Treaty with France and an obdurate French President de Gaulle meant that the Government could not wriggle out of the arrangement. Numerous slurs against TSR.2 continued in the early months of 1965, by which time its flight-test programme was under way with aplomb and 80 per cent of the sophisticated avionics had been developed for the aircraft, with contracts lodged for fifty machines including the nine pre-production development jets. Yet damaging comments prevailed. One such example was the reported announcement by Defence Minister Denis Healey at a Committee Meeting: 'By the way, Prime Minister, we think you should know that the wing of TSR.2 broke under test at Farnborough yesterday.' Somebody had failed to make mention of the fact that the wing was being *deliberately* tested to destruction, as is customary during structural fatigue tests, and had broken at several times its maximum design stress limit! Misinformed about costs, schedules and milestones, it was no wonder two-thirds of the Cabinet were opposed to proceeding with the project that spring. The decision to cancel was taken on 31 March.

The axe formally fell on 6 April 1965 during the Budget Speech in the House of Commons, when the project's cancellation was announced by Chancellor of the Exchequer James Callaghan—apparently tucked between proclamations of an extra sixpence' worth of duty on a packet of cigarettes and four shillings on a bottle of whisky. What especially hurt the workforce was that the BAC Publicity Department knew of the decision beforehand but had been unable to inform their Warton and Weybridge employees on account of a Press embargo.

DESIGN & STRUCTURE

THE WORK SPLIT on TSR.2 had been settled during 1959. Weybridge in Surrey undertook the detailed design of the forward fuselage, cockpit, weapons bay and landing gear subassemblies while Warton in Lancashire created the wings, rear fuselage and engine housing, work on the tail surfaces being split between design at Warton and fabrication at Accrington. This arrangement to a large degree reflected the best of both original competing designs—the Type 571 Vickers fuselage packed with avionics and English Electric's P.17A wings and tail.

While methods of construction made use of the latest technology being adopted by the fledgeling British Aircraft Corporation—for example, numerically controlled (NC) machining—considerable thought was given to the materials employed in TSR.2's manufacture, to cope with both fatigue-inducing stresses resulting from high-speed, low-level flight and temperatures ranging up to 140°C. The final choice settled around aluminium alloys rich in copper. DTD5020 was chosen for frames and panels, and RR58 similarly for the hotter regions around the powerplant, both integrally NC-machined from thick plate, while the revolutionary X2020 was used for formed sheets to skin the airframe. X2020 was a first-generation aluminium-lithium alloy, which the Russians—who ultimately perfected Al-Li alloys for use in fighters like the MiG-29—described as 'as light as cardboard but as strong as steel'. Some concerns existed about its use on TSR.2 because of the reactive nature of lithium and its relative novelty back in the early 1960s. However, TSR.2's American contemporary the RA-5C Vigilante employed Alcoa X2020 in its one-piece wing skins, and twenty years of sea-going salt-water service (a particularly exacting environment) would demonstrate that, given adequate primer and paintwork, the alloy was entirely satisfactory with respect to its resistance to exfoliation and stress

The US Navy's A-5 Vigilante was a near contemporary of the TSR.2 and, like the British aircraft, was—at least, in its original form—a nuclear bomber. In its RA-5C form (below) it served successfully as a reconnaissance platform. The general similarities in configuration of the two designs are striking.

The TSR.2 rear fuselage assembly line at Preston (above), with first (XR660) and second (XR661) pre-production components in the foreground.

corrosion. Titanium was utilised at the hot end of TSR.2, around the 'pen nib' and engine heat shields, and ultra-high-strength vacuum-melted steels were employed for the undercarriage, which assured the integrity of the castings. Temperature-limiting components such as the canopy glazing were fabricated from heat-tolerant alumino-silicates and stretched acrylic laminate, coated with a solar and nuclear-flash protective oxide which lent them a gold appearance. It is worth noting that first- and second-generation low-observable technology was under development at this time in Britain, in the form of embryonic radar-absorbent materials and low-probability-of-intercept defensive, navigation and attack electronics, and this technology remains one of TSR.2's best-kept secrets.

Putting the beautifully engineered sub-assembled pieces together was problematic, not because of match (everything fitted like a glove) but

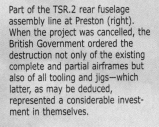

Part of the TSR.2 rear fuselage assembly line at Preston (right). When the project was cancelled, the British Government ordered the destruction not only of the existing complete and partial airframes but also of all tooling and jigs—which latter, as may be deduced, represented a considerable invest-ment in themselves.

Centre fuselage construction at Weybridge (left), showing the intake and main undercarriage bay. In the event, the final intake design owed less to either the Vickers or the English Electric design than to expediency: it was, at the time, considered as good a way as any of dealing with boundary layer air close to the fuselage.

A completed rear fuselage at Preston (below left), showing the huge maws for the Olympus engines and the after portions of the bomb and main undercarriage bays. Most of the remaining space around the powerplants was crammed with fuel.

because of the corporate politics involved, a legacy from the pre-merger era. Warton arguably had the better runway facilities for hot-and-fast jets, but the Vickers team, who had overall control, initially insisted on final assembly taking place at their Brooklands works, despite its tiny airstrip. They then suggested their facility at Wisley. In the end, the aircraft built for flight tests were disassembled and transported by lorry to the Royal Aircraft Establishment at Boscombe Down in Wiltshire for reassembly, check-out and test flight. Production machines, beginning with XS660, would have undergone final pre-acceptance test flights from Warton before being ferried to RAF Coningsby in Lincolnshire (the anticipated base) had the axe not fallen on the programme.

A critical requirement of OR.343 was crew comfort when flying at high speed and low level, and this dictated a small, highly swept, low-aspect-

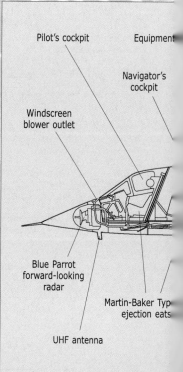

Pilot's cockpit

Equipment

Navigator's cockpit

Windscreen blower outlet

Blue Parrot forward-looking radar

Martin-Baker Typ ejection eats

UHF antenna

TSR.2 wing assembly (right, upper and lower) at Salmesbury. The design of the wing was based principally on English Electric's work, and to imbue the aircraft with satisfactory dutch roll characteristics the tips were downturned. On high-speed aircraft this is normally achieved by giving the entire wing anhedral, but the position of the TSR.2 tailplane—making it vulnerable to the effects of wing wash—demanded some modification of this arrangement.

A cutaway drawing in side elevation of the TSR.2 (below), showing the principal features of the fuselage layout.

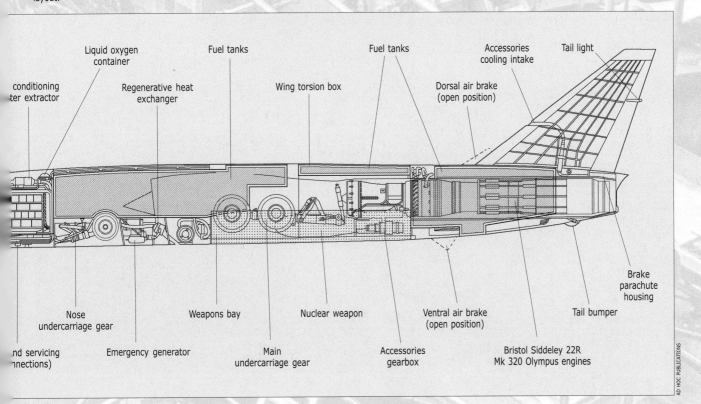

Liquid oxygen container

conditioning ter extractor

Regenerative heat exchanger

Fuel tanks

Wing torsion box

Fuel tanks

Accessories cooling intake

Dorsal air brake (open position)

Tail light

Nose undercarriage gear

Emergency generator

Weapons bay

Main undercarriage gear

Nuclear weapon

Accessories gearbox

Ventral air brake (open position)

Bristol Siddeley 22R Mk 320 Olympus engines

Brake parachute housing

Tail bumper

nd servicing nnections)

The fuselage assembly line at Weybridge (left); the production line at Weybridge shortly before cancellation (below, centre); and the rear fuselage assembly line at Preston (bottom). By the time production of the TSR.2 got under way, the relationship between Vickers-Armstrong and English Electric had been sealed in a company merger, the result being the British Aircraft Corporation. There is no doubt that TSR.2 was the catalyst for the formal marriage of the two partners.

ratio wing offering high loading to reduce bumpiness in the cockpit. The frequency of half-*g* bumps was consequently under one per minute at Mach 0.8. To put that into context, the Buccaneer—the aircraft nicknamed by South African crews the 'Easy Rider' because of its stability and smooth ride—experienced more than a dozen bumps a minute. An important conflicting requirement of TSR.2 was what Sir George described as 'cabbage patch operation'—i.e., dispersed, rough-field performance—dictating the long-legged undercarriage and low-pressure tyres. Operating at weights commensurate with a 450nm radius of action, the machine was expected to get off the ground in a 600-yard roll. The landing gear caused some development difficulties (as outlined elsewhere) but its design did mean that the aircraft's intakes drew air well above the ground—something that

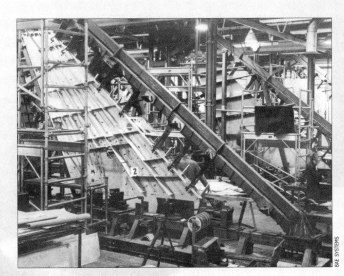

the Americans' squatting F-111 could never do, as it was apt to hoover up any kind of debris and required routinely swept, pristine runways, though it had the advantage of variable-geometry 'swing wings' which moved forward for take-off and backwards, in increments, for high-speed flight. To get airborne as quickly with such a relatively small wing as that developed for TSR.2, full-span, blown flaps were employed, something already featured on Royal Navy Scimitars and the embryonic Buccaneers. The carrier-borne jets had the extra shove of a steam catapult sling to maintain critical momentum at take-off so were able to suffer the drain on their engines, and this remained a Navy feature on both sides of the Atlantic until newer engines came on line. However, because of TSR.2's high thrust-to-weight ratio (0.6:1) with both Olympus powerplants running at full throttle, diverting air from the engine compressors to the flaps had a negligible impact on overall thrust. The challenge was integrating this system into such a thin wing (with approximately 3.6 per cent thickness/chord ratio, compared to the chunkier Naval equivalents). Blowing came on automatically when more than 15 degrees of flap was selected, maintained through the

Production of TSR.2 components was scattered across the country, forward fuselages being produced at Wey-bridge, rear fuselages at Warton, wings at Salmesbury and fins and rudders (top, left and right) at English Electric's Accrington facility; the undercarriage and, of course, the powerplants were produced else-where again. Final assembly was originally to have been undertaken at Weybridge (as shown in the photograph of the first prototype, right), with flight-testing at nearby Wisley, but, in the event, for the early prototypes it was decided to shift these tasks to the Aircraft and Armament Experimental Establish-ment at Boscombe Down, which had a longer runway. Had the programme proceeded beyond the prototype phase, final assembly would have been transferred to Salmesbury and all flight trials conducted at Warton. This tortuous and periphrastic system of aircraft manufacture, though doubtless well-judged in the difficult circumstances, was hardly conducive to efficiency.

full 50-degree flap setting. The two systems guaranteed a superb take-off performance, further assisted by an extending nose gear leg. Nonetheless, those who misunderstood the elegance of TSR.2's blown flaps and thought the shove came purely from the jet engines joked that the arrangement was akin to fitting a Lancaster bomber with Spitfire fighter wings and putting a rocket up its backside! To reduce landing rolls, TSR.2 featured an array of four air brakes mounted on the tail em-

XR219, the first prototype, at Wey-bridge, October 1963 (above, left and right). These were two of the first photographs of the TSR.2 to be released to the public.

pennage, as well as a special Irving-developed parachute featuring a reefing system to allow full- or medium-canopy deployment, permitting the pilot to reduce weathercocking in high crosswinds. If all else failed, the crew could rely on purpose-built Martin Baker Mk 8A zero-zero ejection seats.

The characteristic defining features of TSR.2 comprised its 30-degree drooping wing tips and all-moving tail surfaces. The wing-tip arrange-ment avoided the entire wing having to be slightly sloping in anhedral along its length, necessary on swept wings to preserve good dutch roll behaviour; such would have created a wake which would have interfered with the low-mounted tailplane. The differential all-moving horizontal tail, used for pitch and roll control, also featured separate flaps of its own to maintain control in the wake of the big wing flaps. The rudderless all-moving fin was another major innovation (again shared with the American Vigilante) and comprised a single surface moving about a spigot protruding from the aft fuselage, for directional control. Potential flutter was compensated for by a mass at the apex of the fin and artificial stability; of note, all these controls were power-assisted via the 4,000psi hydraulic system and employed self-adaptive artificial control, so that they responded to pilot inputs appropriately at various

XR219 starts its engines prior to its first flight (above right), and a view of XR220, the second prototype (below) Both photographs were taken at Boscombe Down.

speeds and altitudes. A lot of mathematics went into making these work smoothly and no known problems were encountered throughout the brief but intensive Phase 1 flight-test programme with the hard-worked 'iron bird' XR219. Following cancellation BAC proposed continuing test flights with one of the three completed aircraft at a cost of £2 million, but the Government declined the offer.

POWER

TSR.2's MIGHTY ENGINES, subject to candidate selection alongside the airframe, initially proved to be one of the woes of the project. The two contenders were the Rolls-Royce RB.142 turbofan, which was disqualified by the overseeing committee early in the proceedings, and the Bristol Siddeley Engines (formed out of Bristol Aero Engines and Armstrong Siddeley Motors) Olympus 22R Mk 320, which was a substantially re-engineered, uprated version of the Vulcan B.2's turbojet powerplant with three-stage afterburning added. The Olympus offered 19,600lb (87.2kN) of thrust in full military power (or 'dry') and a colossal 30,610lb (136.2kN) using water-injection and afterburning at sea level. 'Awesome' is the only word that can describe the powerplant: with both engines at full blast, TSR.2 possessed thirty tons of thrust, offering unparalleled take-off performance when coupled with the blown wing, and, crucially, rapid acceleration to get out of trouble if under pursuit. The engines also provided compressed air for the blown wing as well as generating electrical power and pressure for the fuel pumps and hydraulics.

Following 1,900 hours' worth of ground-running tests, Vulcan B.1 XA894 undertook the first of 35 flight tests from Filton with the Olympus 22R mounted in a new ventral engine nacelle, beginning on 23 February 1962, eventually flying on the solitary test article with its own four Olympus 101s throttled back to idle. However, disaster struck at the high-power settings—though fortunately during ground tests. A big bang echoed around northern Bristol as the Vulcan blew up on the tarmac in December 1963, resulting in the machine being subsequently written off through fire damage. The reasons remained misunderstood at the time but became apparent later.

Feeding the engines' two axial-flow compressors was an internal reserve of up to 5,588 Imperial gallons of fuel, combined with air routed from

COLIN WOOD

TSR.2's port intake (below), *sans* Olympus engine. Airflow could be modified by means of the hinged, spiked centrebody and the auxiliary inlets.

The first and second prototypes in final assembly at Weybridge, July 1963 (right). The wing and fin of the first aircraft have been removed to permit the installation of fuel system components.

Vulcan XA894 (below), with the Olympus trials engine mounted underneath, fed with air via bifurcated intakes.

The starboard intake laid bare (right), showing the virgin metal and the mass of access panelling removed.

ROLLS-ROYCE

The port intake stripped down to bare metal, with the lower auxiliary inlet akimbo (left); and a view into the business end of one of the (engineless) tailpipes (below right).

XR219 at Boscombe Down (bottom). One of the requirements of OR.339 was that the aircraft should be capable of operating from dispersed sites, and this would have called for a considerable amount of specially designed support equipment in the shape of general-servicing vehicles, lifting trolleys and hydraulics and systems test apparatus—all complicated by the fact that the aircraft was to be a nuclear bomber.

semi-circular inlet ducts supplied by Joseph Lucas. These sharp-lipped mouths were extended well ahead of the wing, on which shockwaves were kept out of harm's way by means of Vickers' variable-area intakes featuring semi-circular spiked centrebody bullets mounted on hinged wedges fore and aft to control airflow, the gap between functioning as boundary layer bleed when the spike was 'opened', for what soon became apparent as a near-perfect marriage of engine and inlet. Variable-ramp designs, such as those employed on the American Vigilante were experimented with and rejected (though ran a close second). Auxiliary inlet doors (opening just aft of the mouth, like scoops) provided additional air for ground handling and take-off. Together, the engine/inlet combination offered a very impressive initial rate of climb of 50,000 feet a minute,

The cost of this interceptor-like performance was range, and it has been argued that the lighter Rolls-Royce RB.142/3 Medway design, based on both core and bypass flows (a true turbofan), would have greatly expanded this performance parameter.

An Olympus 22R Mk 320 on the test-bench (right). Unlike the development of the TSR.2, that of the Olympus engine culminated in triumph: first run at some 9,000lb in 1956, it evolved over time into the very successful 593 powerplant installed in the Concorde supersonic airliner.

ROLLS-ROYCE

ROLLS-ROYCE

Another view of XR219 taken at Boscombe Down, with British Aircraft Corporation personnel clustered round (below). The aircraft's bomb bay doors are open and the rear main undercarriage door on the port side appears to have been removed.

However, TSR.2 was capable of a 1,000nm 'hi-lo-hi' sortie endurance and a maximum speed in excess of Mach 2 (a factor limited solely by the impact of heat on the windshield and on the radome), and its combat and ferry ranges—the latter pegged at 3,700nm with jettisonable drop tanks—would in any case have been substantially extended by an in-flight refuelling retrofit via a proboscis plumbed into the fuel system, a feature that has long since become standard on RAF combat aircraft. In-flight refuelling was barely beyond its infancy at this juncture, but it would inevitably have been available because it also offered lighter combat take-off weights, with a commensurate increase in safety, take-off payload, climb rate and mission flexibility. Engineering drawings for a retrofit kit had already been devised by the 'boffins' for impending in-service TSR.2s, should the need have arisen.

For operations from austere airfields—TSR.2 was intended to be deployed to such far-flung locations as Aden in the South Yemen, often in advance of the bulk of its support entourage—the aircraft featured a 'pop-down' auxiliary powerplant stowed just forward of the weapons bay. This would be started by a hydraulic motor fed from an accumulator in the aircraft, in turn driving the main engine gearboxes to coax them into action, along with furnishing electrical and hydraulic power to run fuel pumps and 'wake up' the avioncs, obviating the need for starter trolleys.

BAE SYSTEMS

STRIKE AVIONICS

THE WHITE 'anti-flash' scheme complete with pale roundels and fin flashes was intended for TSR.2's primary role of nuclear strike. Operationally, this scheme would quickly have given way to the emerging green and sea grey which was being applied to the RAF 'V-Bomber' fleet as it began to undertake low-level target ingress training in response to the Soviet radar-guided surface-to-air missile (SAM) threat. The main protagonist was the Soviet V75 (or SA-2, NATO codename 'Guideline'), in both conventionally and nuclear tipped versions, together with its probing entourage of radar height-finders and tracking systems. Although deadly at altitude, this SAM was largely incapable of downing jets operating below 500ft above ground level (AGL)—hence the requirement for terrain-following radar (TFR) in TSR.2, to 'hug the contours' beneath this radar/SAM umbrella and yet move fast enough to bypass small-arms and AAA fire about all but the most heavily-defended targets. Ministry requirements—which were far-sighted in this particular respect—determined that 200ft AGL at speeds of up to Mach 1.1 was necessary.

TFR was furnished by Ferranti, based on work with Cornell Aero Laboratories in the United States, which had developed the Autoflite terrain-clearance system. Autoflite was good for avoiding hitting the ground but the American bias towards its mapping function for radar bombing meant that it was apt to make the aircraft vault excessively over the tops of obstacles, exposing it for longer periods and thus render it more vulnerable to a successful SAM engagement. Ferranti's vital contribution was to hone its new monopulse forward-looking radar (FLR), codenamed *Blue Parrot*, for use specifically as a terrain-hugging system (with mapping as a secondary function) using a 'ski toe locus', so that it generated more responsive 'down' commands to the autopilot (known as the Automatic Flight Control System, or AFCS). In the event of a systems hiccough, determined by continuous built-in tests, only 'up' commands would be generated. FLR was roll-stabilised and effective up to 40 degrees of bank angle, and ride 'roughness' was adjustable at the pilot's discretion. Backing

Taxying at Boscombe Down (left). XR219, shown, would later be joined by XR220, but the the event the latter never flew.

this up was a Ferranti radar-altimeter, which looked straight down to give precise height AGL—of particular use when traversing large stretches of water or flat terrain.

The American VERDAN (Versatile Digital Analyzer), or central digital computer, was chosen off-the-shelf to integrate all TSR.2 systems as a 'number cruncher', to calculate navigation and weapons delivery and relay information back to the cockpit displays, offering solid-state electronics technology. Initially failing every quarter of an hour, by the time it was ready for production under licence in the Great Britain by Elliott Automation Ltd (EAL) it was demonstrating a significantly more reassuring 240-hour mean-time-between-failure (MTBF) rate, at which point American Fleet Vigilante pilots had nicknamed it the 'Very Effective Replacement for a Dumb Ass Navigator', such was its speed and reliability. EAL also furnished the all-important AFCS for TSR.2 which was coupled to its FLR, and the head-up display, which projected its symbology directly on to the pilot's tinted windshield instead of a separate glass plate which would otherwise obstruct his view and add to cockpit claustrophobia. The HUD symbology

XR219, the first prototype TSR.2, at Warton following the successful completion of its early flight trials at Boscombe Down, 22 February 1965 (above and right). This was the first occasion that BAC employees at the Lancashire factory had seen the aircraft in its finished state.

BAE SYSTEMS

The first prototype at Warton, 16 July 1965 (above). Typically for the aircraft at rest, the air brakes on the rear fuselage are not fully closed—a recurring problem, apparently.

included all critical information such as airspeed, heading and navigation cues as well as weapons-aiming references. Since TSR.2 was evolving in the era prior to the advent of digital multi-function displays, Smiths Industries supplied an analogue-digital converter and the integrated cockpit panel displays, pioneering the use of now more commonplace electro-luminescent instrument lighting.

Prior to take-off, VERDAN was fed with the crew's carefully pre-planned mission route—containing the waypoints, turning points and objectives in latitude and longitude—by means of punched tape. Up to forty co-ordinates could be programmed into the system, which drove a moving-map display in the cockpit, and flew the aircraft automatically if required by means of AFCS, the latter being simultaneously fed with terrain-hugging information from the FLR. To this extent TSR.2 offered 'hands free' flight after take-off, though the pilot could take manual control whenever required whilst the navigator ensured that the system was constantly updated in order to keep the aircraft on course—especially important in the event of sudden evasive manoeuvres that might take the crew away from their planned course. Despite pilots' jokes about their back-seaters, the navigator was crucial in that he ensured that a pilot did not place undue reliance on everything functioning correctly and perhaps find himself 200 miles from the nearest airstrip with 2,000lb of fuel remaining! Low-level flying, as the ground whizzed by at speed, made staying on course tougher than it would

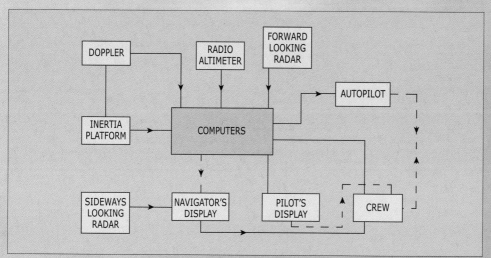

The TSR.2's navigation system (left) was complex and extremely advanced for its day. The heart of the system was the VERDAN computer, the flight plan complete with waypoints being fed into it by means of punched tape prior to take-off. Navigation was fully independent of ground-based assistance, with pre-planned 'fixes' checked by the navigator every 100 or so miles.

Another view of XR219 undergoing ground testing at Boscombe Down (below). The nose undercarriage is in the extended, take-off position.

have been at altitude, where corrections could be effected by visual reference to significant landmarks—estuaries, large rivers, cities. This is where the rest of the 'kit' came into play.

The heart of the navigator's high-technology aids comprised a Ferranti Inertia Reference System (more commonly known now as an Inertial Navigation System, or INS), built around gyros which detected the slightest change in aircraft movement from its pre-computed track and relayed corrective action automatically, via the central nervous system, to the autopilot and displays, providing current position, steering cues and distance-to-go to the next waypoint. The INS was accurate to within two miles over 700 travelled in laboratory conditions, and in the real world normal drift was compensated for by means of inputs from two further sets of sensors in the navigator's armoury—Decca Doppler looking below to measure velocity and drift by means of changes in frequency from the reflected signals, carried out for the most part automatically; and EMI side-looking radars, which provided en-route offset ground mapping and fixes, looking out at ranges of roughly 1–2nm at terrain-hugging heights and further during 'pop-ups' if required. SLR fixes would be accomplished by moving radar cursors on the navigator's display, first on to the 'computed fix' position and then to THE desired point and pressing 'actual fix'. In this way the system was updated—although radar interpretation was a complex skill.

Nuclear bombing would use either the free-fall Low-Altitude Bombing System (LABS) method, whereby release was effected during a 4*g* pull-up manoeuvre to lob the bomb forward to target for air or ground burst while the aircraft rapidly executed a wing-over, back towards safety; or by low-altitude laydown using parachute retarded delivery with or without delayed fusing. These procedures could be accomplished 'blind', based on pre-programmed target co-ordinates, but if there was a visual gathering of the target in the HUD, so much the better. Reversionary manual modes were also available.

At the TSR.2's inception none of this state-of-the-art equipment existed, and it had to be evolved largely from scratch. Original cost estimates were thus ridiculously low and much was made of this by the aircraft's detractors, resulting in over-management by the infamous Governmental committee system already alluded to.

WEAPONS & COUNTERMEASURES

A NEW FAMILY of British nuclear weapons was in development at this time, designated WE.177 and entering RAF service some two years after TSR.2 ultimately was abandoned, to be used by the giant Vulcan B.2 and later the newer but comparatively primitive Buccaneer S.2. WE.177 came in both free-fall and parachute-retarded models for loft and lay-down deliveries. This would have been TSR.2's primary nuclear deterrent, and it is interesting to note that WE.177 remained in service until mid-1998, which gives some indication of how long TSR.2 would have maintained its nerve-shivering role. Much of the anti-TSR.2 lobby was focused around the gargantuan cost of providing precision sensors and avionics to deliver such nuclear horror; in reality, however, the major cost was a result of the need to deliver conventional high-explosive weapons precisely, using dive, dive-toss (following a 'pop-up' from terrain-hugging flight) and lay-down visual methods offering a 50 per cent CEP of as little as 250ft (that is, half the bombs would fall within that distance of the aimpoint, if aimed correctly and povided all the switches had been set properly).

Conventional weapons options included up to six 1,000lb 'iron' bombs in the 20ft-long weapons bay, pre-loaded in threes on two clip-in carriers that would be hoisted into place using built-in winches, with up to four more weapons underwing. The bombs embraced the new retarded version, allowing delivery at 200ft AGL at speeds ranging as high as transonic, by means of cruciform air brakes and a parachute which popped out after release in 'belt and braces' fashion. The American equivalent was the Mk 82 Snakeye, a 500lb cruciform-retarded bomb with a 500kt safe delivery limit. The TSR.2 pilot had control of these weapons ,which would be delivered for the most part visually using the HUD as an aiming reference, after the

The first prototype is waved in at Warton after landing from its flight from Boscombe Down, 22 February 1965 (right).

TSR.2's 20-foot-long weapons bay could accommodate a variety of warloads (below), each arranged as a 'pre-packaged' cluster to be, literally, clipped into position. The wing hardpoints were, it is reported, each stressed for 2,500lb. In service, the aircraft would have replaced the so-called 'V-bombers' in the nuclear role, armed with the standard British ordnance of the day, initially—and for a short period only—'Red Beard' and subsequently WE.177.

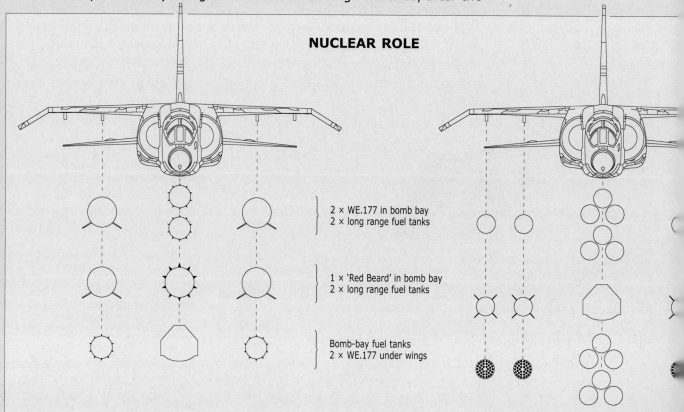

NUCLEAR ROLE

2 × WE.177 in bomb bay
2 × long range fuel tanks

1 × 'Red Beard' in bomb bay
2 × long range fuel tanks

Bomb-bay fuel tanks
2 × WE.177 under wings

CONVENTIONAL ROLE

6 × 1,000lb 'iron' bombs in bomb bay
4 × 1,000lb 'iron' bombs under wings

Bomb bay fuel tanks
4 × Martel AGM

6 × 1,000lb 'iron' bombs in bomb bay
4 × SNEB under wings

AD HOC PUBLICATIONS

navigator in the back had pre-selected the stores stations and release interval, although radar blind-bombing was also on offer. The four external pylon hardpoints were stressed to each carry either additional 1,000lb bombs (and would have worked equally well with BL.755 cluster bomb units and Paveway II laser-guided munitions) or 2in SNEB rocket packs, though the idea of using a machine as sophisticated as TSR.2 to deliver rack-of-the-eye rockets in a diurnal close air support role, amidst a hail of anti-aircraft fire, was somewhat antiquated even for its day! Such weaponry as SNEB would mostly have been expended during firepower demonstrations to visiting dignitaries, or in low-threat areas. To this end, provisions for air-to-surface guided weapons (ASGW) were wired in, allowing stand-off attack beyond the reach of most hostile fire. The principal ASGW envisaged was the Anglo-French Martel (Missile Anti-Radar, Television), developed jointly by Hawker Siddeley Dynamics, Nord Aviation and Matra beginning in September 1964, which came in two principal flavours and whose impetus from the British perspective was driven by TSR.2. The first was the predominantly British AJ.168 TV-guided version, whereby the navigator would slew the missile's TV vidicon sensor so that the chosen target slid under his display 'grid' and was locked-on prior to launch, the pilot having first rolled the aircraft in on the appropriate attack heading. Mid-course corrections would then be possible by joystick after launch by means of a microwave data-link (a later feature), leaving the attack crew free to stay

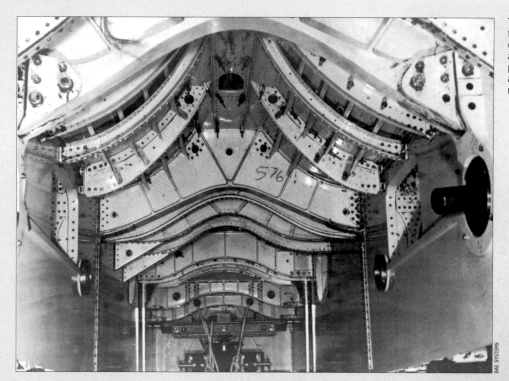

The TSR.2's bomb bay, looking forward (left). The suite carried could comprise weapons, additional fuel or a specially designed reconnaissance pack. This is the bay of an incomplete airframe: the doors, for example, are not yet fitted.

beyond arm's length while delivering a lethal punch. The second Martel type was the principally Gallic AS.37 radar-homing variant, designed to lock-on passively to, then guide towards, enemy emitters unaided, and disable them. It could be pre-programmed to home on anticipated threats, or sweep through known hostile frequencies when activated in flight. Stand-off attack range was in the order of up to 30 miles. Although Martel took many more years to mature in its various guises, it was an extremely sophisticated ASGW and, according to engineers who worked on the programme, at least seven years in advance of contemporary American 'smart' weapons.

Last but not least, TSR.2 was equally revolutionary in offering the RAF their first high-performance combat jet with built-in passive electronic countermeasures (ECM), integrated with its identification and communications systems. This Category One equipment, devised mostly by Government and industry 'boffins', was fitted in the nose, tail and wing and included a complete suite of HF/UHF communications, as well as

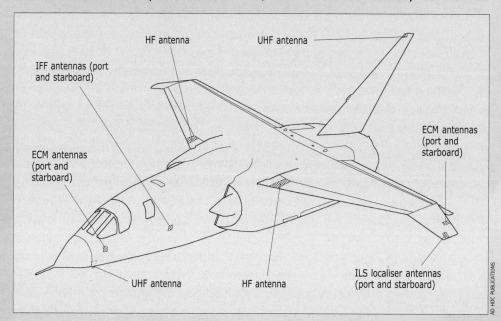

The communications system (left)—multi-channel HF/VHF/UHF and standby UHF transmitters and receivers, plus SIF and ECM transponders of the latest technology.

BAE SYSTEMS

The first TSR.2, XR219, is readied for flight at A&AEE Boscombe Down (above). Ground servicing equipment—some standard, some extemporary—is scattered around as last-minute adjustments are made. The bomb bay doors are open.

Looking aft along the bomb bay of XR222 (below) as it appears today.

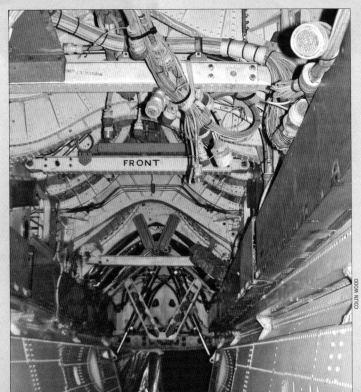

COLIN WOOD

sophisticated Identification Friend or Foe (IFF) interrogation equipment (known as the Special Identification Facility, or SIF). TSR.2's brand of wideband ECM, more specifically referred to as a radar warning receiver, was designed to pick up tell-tale electromagnetic illumination by hostile radar defences, and alert the crew to change course or take evasive action, and even adjust onboard TFR or SLR radar output to minimise detection. It listened in the short, compromise, and x-marks-the-spot wavelength range of between 2.5 and 18 gigacycles, distinguishing threats operating in the E through to J pulse repetition frequency bands. In a nutshell, it meant the crew would be alerted by means of warning lamps to both ground threats such as 'Fan Song', associated with the ubiquitous Soviet SA-2 SAM, and with higher-frequency radars such as 'Jay Bird', associated with Mach 2-capable MiG-21 'Fishbed' interceptors. Active ECM, to thwart radars and missiles by means of radio-frequency jamming and expendable pyrotechnics such as chaff ('window') and flares, would inevitably, in time, have been carried in podded form under the wings—as they would be on its 'replacements' the Buccaneer and Tornado a good deal later, when bought mostly off-the-shelf from Sweden and America beginning in 1973. Next to nothing is known about contemporary British development of these systems and the aircraft's back-up SIF signals intelligence-gathering capabilities, as they remain classified to this day. It is important to remember that, while such devices are commonplace nowadays, they were unheard of forty years ago except for use by the biggest and most expensive strategic bombers, which tinkered with updated World War II-era radio countermeasures technology. In the wake of TSR.2's cancellation, the RAF would, electronically speaking, fly virtually naked for almost a further decade.

TWENTY-SEVEN

FLIGHT

THE REAL TEST, of course, came with TSR.2 XR219's maiden flight, which was fraught with potential danger and which incurred considerable soul-searching on behalf of the engineers and test crew. The key issue resulting in the loss of the Vulcan platform and two ground failures, including a major one in August 1964 which blew the test house apart, was resonance—vibration—resulting from the newly uprated power shaft ringing like a bell at sustained full power settings. Test pilot and World War II ace Roland ('Bea') Beamont and his back-seat engineer Don Bowen stoically climbed aboard XR219 on 27 September 1964 for the maiden flight knowing that the machine might explode around them if maximum thrust were piled on for too long. Throttle settings were therefore limited to 97 per cent after the tense take-off run and climb but might have had to be sustained or reintroduced in the event of one engine quitting, as the landing gear was not yet qualified for retraction.

In the event, the first flight went magnificently well. One of the two photographic chase Canberras lost sight of the white projectile almost immediately after take-off while the chase Lightning struggled to keep pace and was left behind! The only problem to appear occurred on landing. The stalky legs, designed for rough-field performance, introduced a nauseating lateral vibration which rocked the crew violently. It took much time to correct and was compounded by other problems such as the main gear tandem wheel bogies not rotating to the correct position on sortie No 5 on 14 January 1965, resulting it what was described as a perfect tip-toed landing on the forward main wheels using a gentle (and astonishing) 6-inch-per-second sink rate. Jimmy Dell, who took the machine aloft on Flight 6 the following day for familiarisation and for low-speed handling trials, had the gear locked down but experienced a recalcitrant right-hand landing leg on Flight 7 on 22 January. Low-speed stability trials occupied Flights 8 and 9 on 23 and 27 January, respectively, when the test pilots and long-suffering back-seater Bowen demonstrated full-flap landings.

The big white bird finally takes to the air, 27 September 1964 (below and right, upper), although it would be some months before difficulties with the undercarriage retraction mechanism were resolved (right, lower).

BAE SYSTEMS

Undercarriage raising and lowering was not demonstrated as satisfactory until the tenth flight, on 6 February with 'Bea' in charge, when the machine was thrust to its flutter limit of 500 knots indicated airspeed. The difficulty had been fully resolved by Flight 22 on 26 March during numerous practice approaches and landing-gear cycles.

Modified Olympus engines had been introduced for Flight 2, which took place on 31 December 1964, the engine 'ringing' having been cured by the end of November. The crew's vision was disturbed again when oscillation from the No 1 fuel pump caused a ghastly resonance at 35Hz in sympathy with the human eyeball, and as a result Beamont aborted the flight and landed on one engine. The pump was replaced. The third flight took place two days later with that problem fixed, but a false warning light, indicating imminent engine shaft failure, put the wind up the crew. Flight 4 on 8 January 1965 demonstrated this problem as resolved.

TSR.2's highly complex landing gear caused innumerable headaches (above, below left, and right). For operations from semi-prepared strips—as demanded by the specification—the aircraft required low-pressure, large-diameter tyres, in turn necessitating capacious wheel bays, the volume of which had already been stretched in order to accommodate the double-cycle retraction mechanism. It took much work and several flights before the undercarriage gear could be retracted with confidence.

Further images showing the first prototype in flight (left, above, and below)—well into the trials programme and now with the undercarriage safely tucked up.

With the undercarriage issues also cured, the test programme entered a much more confident phase, and during the remaining fourteen flights undertaken by TSR.2 the performance envelope was quickly opened, troubled only by minor fuel leaks which were fixed. Don Knight joined as test pilot for Flight 12, and by Flight 14 on 22 February 'Bea' Beamont and Peter Moneypenny took the machine through the sound barrier to Mach 1.12. Low-level sorties down to 200 feet above the Pennines, full rolls and speeds of up to 600 knots indicated airspeed were also displayed. Yaw and roll were optimised on what transpired to be the final flight, No 24, on 31 March 1965. It was an incredible achievement to accomplish all this in the space of a flight-test programme lasting a mere six months with just one available aircraft.

R IS FOR RECONNAISSANCE

RECONNAISSANCE was part and parcel of the stringent requirements of OR.343, was considered to be of equal importance to the aircraft's strike role, and stipulated a day-and-night, medium- and low-altitude capability—which entailed some revolutionary new technology. While TSR.2 was permanently fitted with its nose installation of navigation radars and near-standard RAF F.95 framing cameras (looking out from both sides and down), a sensor pallet was devised which was intended to be 'clipped in' the weapons bay in lieu of bombs for dedicated reconnaissance missions. This was to be routinely installed—though the suite itself was only ever tested on surrogate aircraft—by the simple expedient of removing the weapons bay doors and hoisting and locking the entire unit into place, in a 'swing-role' manner. A TSR.2 so fitted would have been distinguishable from an aircraft in the strike configuration by means of its ventral sensor 'canoe', which had a negligible impact on the machine's flight performance. The suite was lauded as unmatched for its day, offering 'high-grade target intelligence . . . by day and by night regardless of weather conditions'. The reconnaissance pack was controlled by the navigator using two slot-in cockpit panels (replacing weapons control units on that mission) and was split into forward and aft compartments, the front end housing power and recording units along with an optical linescanner and the rear a trio of F.126 cameras and a radio link.

Along most of the length of the housing ran EMI Q-band sideways-looking reconnaissance radar (SLRR) featuring large-aperture 15ft-long aerials which, because of their size, could generate high-definition radar maps on photographic film. This would demand absolutely straight and level flight, but the antennas' depression look angle could be adjusted by the navigator. Looking left and right—or to only one side, in a 'stand-off' manner—the SLRR would have generated swathes of imagery up to 10nm wide, with enough film on board to cover a length of 1,500nm (though, for obvious reasons, significantly shorter runs would have been usual in a tactical operational environment) at a scale of 5nm per inch. The film was processed after recovery and the idea would be to get the recce products to field commanders within two hours of the original request. Crucially,

Shepherded by its Canberra chase plane, XR219, its brake parachute streaming, lands back as Boscombe after the first flight (right).

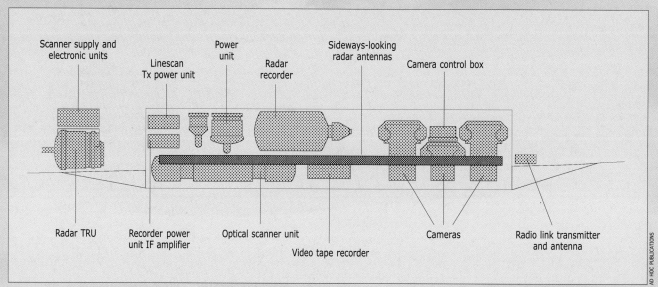

Scanner supply and electronic units

Power unit

Sideways-looking radar antennas

Linescan Tx power unit

Radar recorder

Camera control box

Radar TRU

Recorder power unit IF amplifier

Optical scanner unit

Video tape recorder

Cameras

Radio link transmitter and antenna

AD HOC PUBLICATIONS

The optional reconnaissance pack was designed to clip in to the weapons bay, its various systems serviceable via access panels along its length (left). Elsewhere, permanent camera equipment, though of relatively limited capability, was installed in the aircraft's forward fuselage.

SLRR could be used to generate Moving Target Indicator (MTI) intelligence at lower altitudes, to pick up vehicles moving as slowly as 10mph against the ground. In this format the developed film showed both radar map imagery and MTI side by side along its length, annotated with co-ordinates from the navigation system, thus making relatively light work of target interpretation. Generally, SLRR would work as a search sensor and in wartime repeated runs over set areas of interest would be established at intervals to be fed into the intelligence network.

For high-definition daytime photography the pack's three FX.126 cameras came into play. Also still very much in development in parallel with TSR.2, two cameras were optimised for medium-altitude reconnaissance, fitted with lenses of either 36in or 24in focal length, while the third would customarily have been fitted with a stubbier lens of 6in focal length, all offering the equivalent of an interpretation scale of 1:10,000 when used at operating heights of 30,000ft, 20,000ft and 10,000ft, respectively—enough to classify ships and SAM complexes—and commensurately smaller inter-pretation scales with significantly greater image detail at lower altitude, sufficient to record and classify individual armoured vehicles. Pin-sharp pictures were possible with all lenses by means of image movement compensation and autoexposure so that frames could be shot at speeds of Mach 1.3 as low as 1,250ft AGL. The film magazine cassettes contained 250ft of film, enough to capture up to 4,050 square nautical miles in the high-altitude 'survey' mode. Film was again annotated with geographic co-ordinates and important data such as camera look angle. The imagery from these was, of course, supplemented by any shots taken using 3in focal length F.95 optics in the nose of the machine, customarily employed for bomb damage assessment or air-to-air snaps.

Linescanner was the *pièce de résistance* in the kit. Built by EMI, this worked as both a passive daytime *and* an active night-time imaging sensor, using a fast-spinning mirror which, at 1,000ft AGL, scanned successive strips of ground a nautical mile wide beneath TSR.2 as the jet plied its course, and projected these onto a photo-electric cell. This device simply converted the variations in light intensity it received, line by line, into an electrical signal which could be collected on an airborne video tape recorder for post-mission down-loading or transmitted back to a ground-receiving station up to 120 miles away, virtually instantaneously, via a steerable data-link aerial built into the rear of the sensor canoe. On the ground the signals would be converted back into monochrome prints, also annotated with aircraft height, position and other parameters. What was special was its night-time function. For nocturnal reconnaissance duties the linescanner activated a high-intensity light which would scan via a second rotating mirror in synchronism with the receiving one, effectively lighting the scene below line-by-line in sympathy. Movement of the spot on the ground was so rapid that it did not betray the aircraft's location, being undetectable to normal vision. This science-fiction device produced startling imagery approaching that gleaned by conventional cameras by day and night, but without the use of the tell-tale photo-flash required by conventional cameras for night-time work (which proved dead give-aways in TSR.2's would-be contemporaries the American McDonnell RF-4 Photo-Phantom II and the North American RA-5 Vigilante and which rapidly fell into disfavour amongst

The complete reconnaissance suite with the aircraft configured for that specific role (left); the wing stations would of course be available for ordnance or additional fuel, as demanded by the sortie.

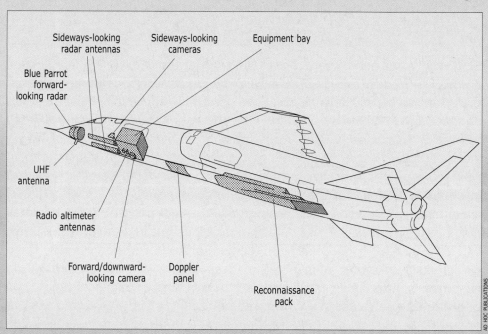

Sideways-looking radar antennas

Sideways-looking cameras

Equipment bay

Blue Parrot forward-looking radar

UHF antenna

Radio altimeter antennas

Forward/downward-looking camera

Doppler panel

Reconnaissance pack

AD HOC PUBLICATIONS

TSR.2 XR219 during an early test flight, with air brakes deployed (above). The larger (aftermost) main undercarriage doors snapped back shut once the leg had deployed, in order to maximise aerodynamics and to discourage the ingress of rubbish into the bay if the aircraft were operating from rough airstrips. The streaming vortices demonstrate beyond doubt the effectiveness of the anhedral wing tips in keeping turbulent wing wash well clear of the tailplane.

combat crews in Vietnam). Desperate for night-time photography, almost a decade after Britain evolved the concept, the United States Air Force tested active linescanner linked to low-altitude panoramic cameras aboard ten RF-4Cs, under its 'Compass Count' programme. Designated the AN/AVD-2 Laser Reconnaissance Set and field-trialled between 1969 and 1974, this system ultimately was not adopted because of intervening advances in infra-red linescanner (IRLS) technology, which used a heat-sensitive diode which otherwise worked along similar principles to Britain's pioneering linescanner. IRLS offered the advantages of being able to work day and night in a purely passive mode (presenting no problems with an overheated laser which might malfunction) and to generate more tactically useful information as it was able to differentiate between warm and cold and thus see through camouflage netting and vegetation, to a degree, enabling interpreters to distinguish operationally active targets from inert or dummy ones, the contents of ships and storage facilities and so forth. IRLS became *de rigueur* by the mid-1970s on top-echelon reconnaissance jets, and TSR.2 would, without question, have soon adopted this system in service (as did the Canberra PR.9 with the ARI 5969). However, contemporary IRLS was recorded on film and therefore, unlike linescanner, could only be scrutinised after the aircraft had been recovered and its film had been wet-developed, just like the

RICHARD L. WARD

film from SLRR and conventional cameras and therefore making it less timely. IRLS was also severely degraded at dawn and dusk, when the sun's grazing angle is low. In service, operational TSR.2s would probably have enjoyed both linescanning systems: the aircraft certainly had the requisite growth capacity.

TSR.2's interim replacement in the RAF, the McDonnell Phantom FGR.2, carried some of what was intended for TSR.2's reconnaissance module repackaged in a big, 2,300lb pod built by EMI and including an F.126 camera and Type P391 Q-Band SLRR (along with Texas Instruments RS-700 IRLS in lieu of linescanner). These replaced the centreline fuel 'bag' on selected Phantoms assigned to No II (Army Co-operation) Squadron based at RAF Laarbruch on the German/Dutch border, and to No 41 Squadron at RAF Coningsby in Lincolnshire, becoming operational from 1971 and staying in service until supplanted by SEPECAT Jaguars in the reconnaissance role five years later (merely so as to liberate the Phantoms for crucial air defence duties). The EMI-podded F-4s were considered the best reconnaissance platforms in the RAF for use in heavily-defended 'hot' areas and yet carried less than half of TSR.2's gear, with significant performance disadvantages because of the external pod.

In this area, at least, all was not for naught. Elements of the reconnaissance system continued in service for the ensuing two decades in various 'strap on' pods and aboard the RAF's Canberra fleet. However, near real-time data-linked intelligence of the type offered by TSR.2's cancelled linescanner remained a pipe-dream until the advent of modern digital imaging in the 1980s, and with further development Britain might have

Some of TSR.2's specially developed reconnaissance equipment found its way several years later into the pod developed for the Phantom FGR.2 (above). However, this was a rather less capable fitting than TSR.2's, and, having to be carried externally, imposed a serious drag penalty on the aircraft.

The reconnaissance 'workhorse' of the US Air Force for thirty years beginning in 1964 was the McDonnell RF-4C Photo-Phantom II (below), some 505 of which were delivered into service. Active optical linescanner equipment was tested on selected aircraft assigned to the 12th TRS at Tan Son Nhut, Republic of Vietnam, between 1969 and 1971.

BOEING

XR219 soars skywards during a test flight (above), flaps partially down, auxiliary intake doors open and air brakes not quite shut—the last another 'little local difficulty' that took some effort to cure.

Even with the project's cancellation, the taxpaying public were deemed unworthy of viewing TSR.2 until XR222—minus various fittings and equipment and some panelling— appeared at a Royal College of Aeronautics pageant in September 1973 (below).

become a world-leader in such reconnaissance imaging electronics, now mostly bought off-the-shelf from the United States. This clearly indicates just how advanced TSR.2 was in its time. With inevitable hindsight, it equally illustrates just how frustrating it must have been for the RAF to suffer the loss of TSR.2's 'R' component as well as its strike capabilities. As for pseudo-strategic 'survey' work, in TSR.2's absence, the long-suffering Canberra PR.9s stationed at RAF Wyton would be rebuilt by Shorts of Belfast to soldier on for almost a further three decades. The signals-gathering element of TSR.2's capabilities, which were linked to its ECM, remain classified to this day.

INSIDE INFORMATION

Details of the TSR.2 pilot's cockpit (right and opposite), showing the flight instruments and the main features of the side consoles. The layout was conventional by the standards of the day but included an OR.946 director navigation display and a moving-map indicator. There was also a basic head-up display (HUD) offering the pilot flight, speed, attack mode and essential take-off/landing information.

Each crew member was provided with the Martin-Baker Type 8A ejection seat (below), designed specifically for—and unique to—the aircraft. The photograph in the centre depicts the rear of the seat.

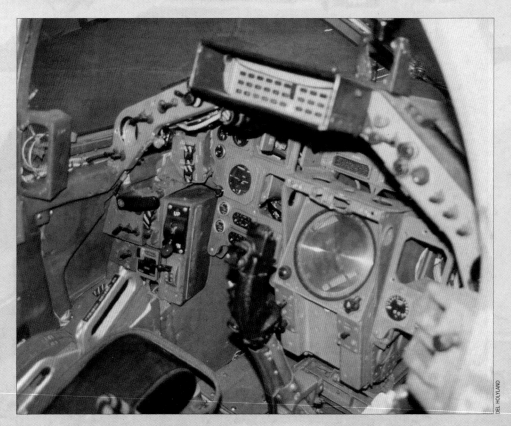

DEL HOLYLAND

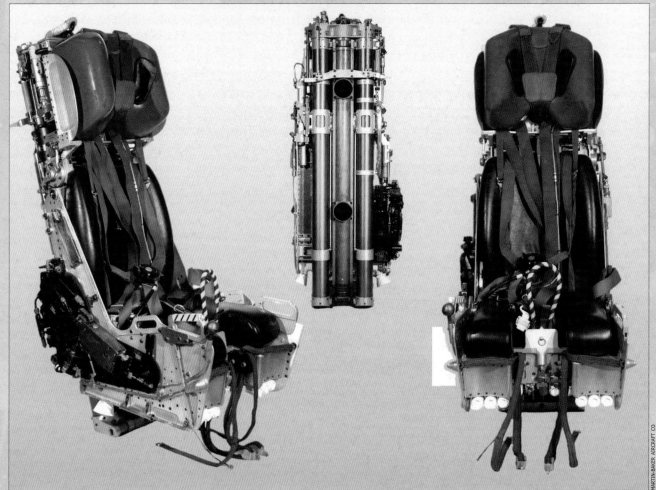

MARTIN-BAKER AIRCRAFT CO

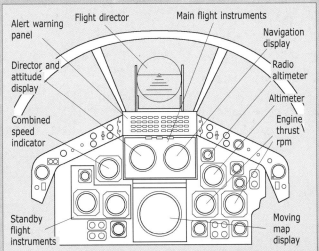

Alert warning panel

Flight director

Main flight instruments

Navigation display

Director and attitude display

Radio altimeter

Altimeter

Engine thrust rpm

Combined speed indicator

Standby flight instruments

Moving map display

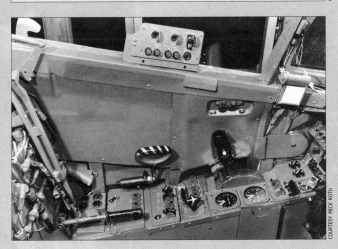

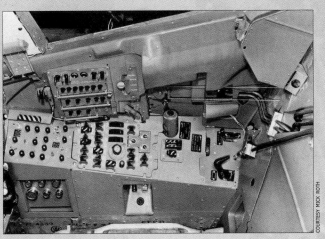

XR219's cockpit being fitted out (opposite page). The windscreen has protection against damage and the canopies can be seen lying in front of the nose of the aircraft.

The navigator's cockpit is depicted above and at left, dominated by the central radar display. In the event of ejection (bottom), the pilot could evict both crew members but the navigator only himself. A delay sequence was programmed into the system so that, if both crewmen needed to eject at once, the navigator would precede his companion by a few seconds in order to minimise the chances of interference or collision one with the other. Activation of the ejection ring would automatically jettison the canopies prior to the departure of the seats.

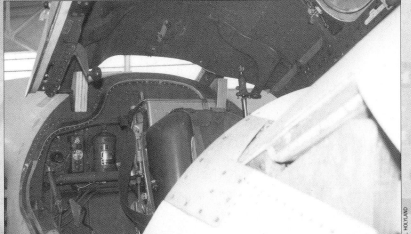

LEGACY

ONLY ONE EXAMPLE of TSR.2 ever flew, XR219, the exciting trials and tribulations of which have already been described. XR220, the second example, had been delivered to Boscombe Down in Wiltshire in September 1964 in bits but an important fuselage section had been partially damaged when the trailer on which it was being conveyed jack-knifed, causing the machine to fall on its tail spigot. It was repaired over the ensuing months, and test pilot Jimmy Dell was all set to take the assembled jet aloft on the same fateful day that the project was abruptly terminated, and so it never flew. In an unparalleled demonstration of paranoia, lest the project be resurrected by a future administration, the Wilson Government ordered that all construction jigs be cut up, the wooden mock-up be burnt and the two completed and three virtually complete airframes be transported to the Shoeburyness target range. XR219 eventually succumbed as a target at Foulness in the early 1970s before its remnants were finally disposed of during 1982. XR221 and XR223 were dumped at Shoeburyness and finally scrapped by 1973. Remnants of the sub-assemblies for the remaining four pre-production examples and eleven additional machines contracted for in June 1963, together with long-lead components for the thirty aircraft ordered in March 1964, were either scrapped or survive as nondescript remnants at Farnborough and Halton, or in fragments on the target ranges. Fortuitously, XR220 survived intact and is currently exhibited at the Cosford Aerospace Museum, whilst XR222 similarly escaped destruction by finding its way to the Cranfield College of Aeronautics in October 1965. In 1978 it was presented to the Imperial War Museum at Duxford, near Cambridge, and it is set to go on display again alongside examples of the Vulcan and Concorde in the AirSpace Hangar (due to open in 2007), which is to pay homage to British aviation as equal exemplar of British ingenuity.

Not long after project cancellation, and in an effort to placate the RAF, the Government placed an order for fifty American General Dynamics 'swing wing' F-111Ks (on the heels of the Royal Australian Air Force, which had ordered two dozen of their own in the knowledge that TSR.2—which they

Such was the determination of the 1964–66 Wilson administration to do away with the TSR.2 programme that its directives went far beyond mere cancellation: in what can only be described as a fit of paranoia unique in modern British political history, all traces of the project were ordered to be wiped out, the bizarre instructions being 'not to leave any piece . . . bigger than a fist'. Here (right) components await final disposal at Salmesbury.

The second pototype, XR220, never made it into the air although had the cancellation of the project been announced twenty-four hours later it might well have done. Here (left), its wings clipped—metaphorically and literally—it departs unceremoniously from Boscombe Down

BAE SYSTEMS

XR219 suffered a demeaning end—as a subject for target practice in the Essex marshes (below). The pretext for the programme's cancellation—too great a financial burden on the British taxpayer—in the event proved laughable: the British Government's order for its 'cheaper' alternative, the American F-111K, had also to be cancelled, ostensibly for the same reason. The Australians ended up paying out some £4–5 million apiece for their 24 aircraft, so the invoice for the British order for fifty would hardly have been less than £200 million—twice the cost of the TSR.2 programme to date. F-111K cancellation costs were of course money wasted, and the aircraft eventually bought, the F-4M Phantom, reputedly cost an extra £5 million per unit merely to fit it with Rolls-Royce engines. In comparison, TSR.2 would have been a positive bargain—and far superior in terms of capability.

wanted—would never enter production). These were cancelled in 1968 at great cost to the taxpayer owing to problems with this troubled Texan and the decision to withdraw from 'East of Suez'. The RAAF received their simpler F-111Cs several years late, in 1973, yet to its credit the type remains the most important component in the RAAF's strike arsenal even today, bolstered by ex-USAF airframes and a reinvigorating digital avionics update; it is set to bow out of service very shortly after four decades of continuous employment. By comparison the RAF were left with a void: attempts to foster an Anglo-French Variable-Geometry (swing-wing) effort alongside the civil Concorde programme led to naught, though did result in orders for the SEPECAT Jaguar, a sophisticated and nimble daytime close air support/battle area interdiction and reconnaissance jet which, after Warton had got their hands on it, bore few similarities to its French training jet origins. The introduction of the Jaguar, moreover, freed just over a hundred surviving supersonic Phantom FGR.2s for the air defence role, these having been press-ganged into ground-attack and reconnaissance duties from 1968 as 'interim' Canberra replacements; while, in a further ironic twist, S.2 models of Mountbatten's beloved carrier-based Buccaneer were

BIPPA

ASSOCIATED NEWSPAPERS

grudgingly accepted into RAF service from the beginning of the following year. Devoid of any sophistication whatsoever, but considered to be delightful aircraft by the crews who flew and maintained them, the Buccaneers held down the fast-and-low nuclear and conventional strike roles until the Anglo-German-Italian Panavia Tornado became available from 1979. These, in turn, are now giving way to the Anglo-German-Italian-Spanish Eurofighter Typhoon, spawned as the European Fighter Aircraft.

GENERAL DYNAMICS

Multi-million-pound scrapheap (above): TSR.2 airframe sections at a junkyard in 1966.

RAFPR

TSR.2's 'cheaper' substitute—the troubled F-111 (left, upper; the -F variant is shown). Fifty F-111Ks were ordered for the RAF and two almost got to flight-test stage before the British Government pulled out of the deal. BAC's recovery programme eventually took the form of partnership in producing the Anglo-French Jaguar strike fighter/trainer (left, lower)—a very worthy and capable aircraft as it turned out, but no TSR.2.

The true successor to the TSR.2, after a number of false starts (including the AFVG) was the MRCA (right), which evolved into the Tornado. This aircraft—not without tribulation—eventually entered service with the RAF in the early 1980s.

In the meantime, the heritage of irony associated with the TSR.2 project continues to this day: Warton's English Electric Canberra, the aircraft that the handsome white bomber was supposed to replace, is still in RAF service, albeit admittedly not in its bomber role. The much re-worked PR Mk 9, a handful of which are based at RAF Marham in Norfolk with No 39 Squadron, will continue to take photographs until 2006, when the aircraft is, finally, to be retired.

Against the odds (below): the second prototype, XR220, having miracu-lously escaped axe and blow-torch, en route for preservation at Cosford, 22 May 1975.

At the Pierson Memorial Lecture held by the Royal Aeronautical Society in October 1989, speaker M. W. Salisbury quoted test pilot Roland Beamont: '. . . without the challenge and stimulus of the TSR.2 in the 1960s, the technology vitally needed for the Tornado and EFA might well not have been available in this country.' Salisbury, who had been intimately involved in the TSR.2 project, concluded that, in his belief, 'it was also essential to today's situation in non-technical areas such as industrial co-operation, project management and production technology. So, perhaps, those seven years of some of our lives were not wasted after all.' The true legacy is a vital powerplant and avionics industry in Britain, coupled to leading-edge design and fabrication of critical aircraft components, including world-beating wings and landing gear. Every time one witnesses an Airbus airliner or Typhoon go about its business, there's a little bit of TSR.2 in there.

SAVED

IN THE EVENT, not everything relating to the TSR.2 programme was immediately destroyed. The completed XR220 and the virtually complete fourth aircraft, XR222, escaped altogether. Parts of other airframes also survive, notably an anonymous forward fuselage at Brooklands, near Weybridge, and there are reputedly other small bits and pieces of airframe gathering dust at other locations. These remnants of the most technologically brilliant—but most politically vilified—aircraft programme in British history serve as a reminder of what could, and should, have been.

XR220, superbly restored, now resides in the RAF collection as Cosworth (this spread). It is reportedly the more complete of the two surviving aircraft, including within its airframe much if not most of the internal equipment.

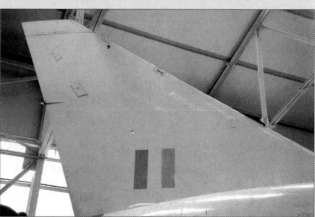

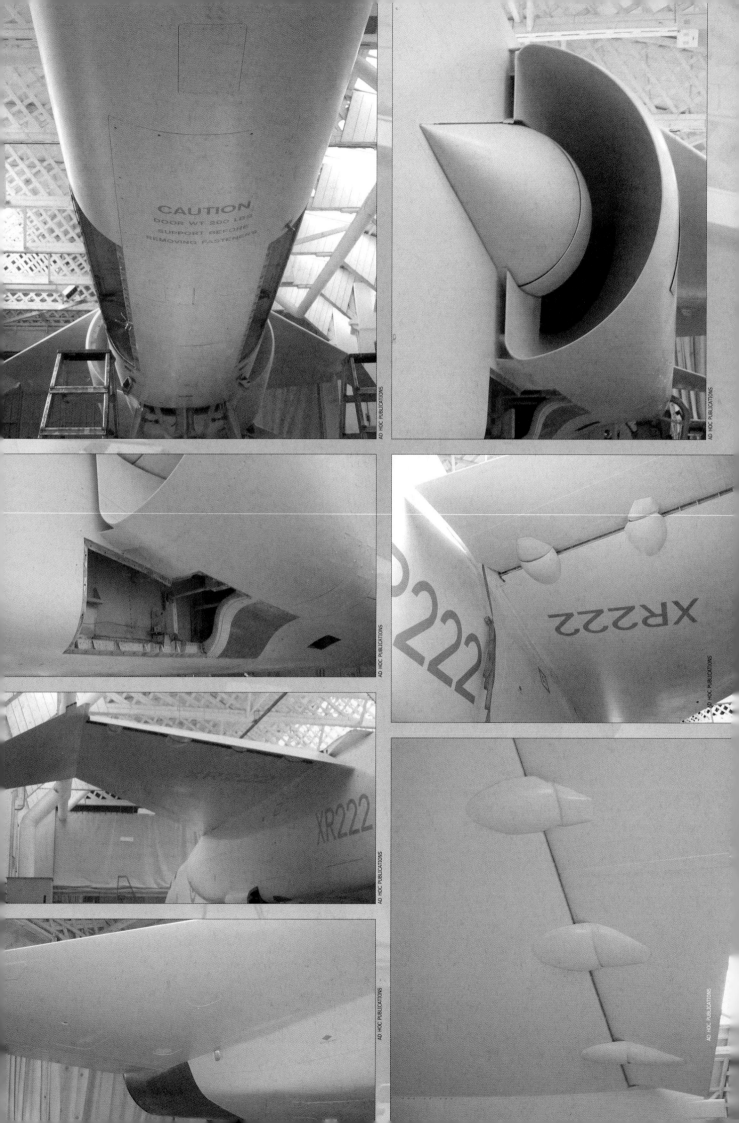

CAUTION
DOOR WT 200 LBS
SUPPORT BEFORE
REMOVING FASTENERS

222

XR222

XR222

The Imperial War Museum at Duxford has the only other intact TSR.2, XR222 (this spread), at the time of writing completing its restoration for permanent display, under cover. The aircraft lacked its fin and other fittings when these photographs were taken in August 2005, but a magnificent (and costly) repainting task had just been completed, all colours being precisely to the original specifications.

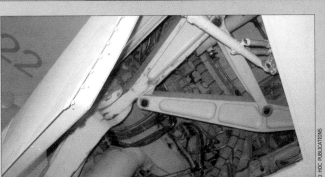

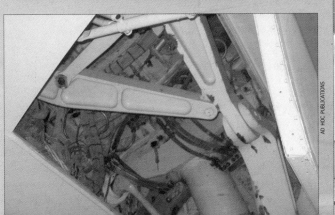

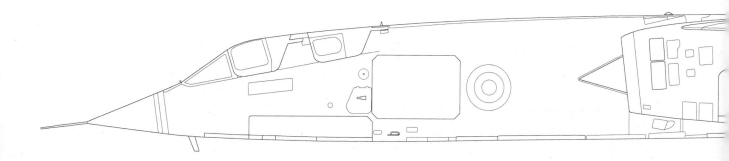

TSR.2 OUTLINE SPECIFICATIONS

Engines	Two Bristol Olympus B.01.22R each rated at 16,600lb (normal) or 30,600lb (with afterburner)
Dimensions	Length (overall) 89ft 0½in; wingspan 37ft 1½in; height 23ft 9in; wing area 702.9 sq ft
Weights	54,750lb empty; 96,000lb take-off (typical)
Performance	
Maximum speed	840mph at sea level (Mach 1.1); over 1,350mph (Mach 2) at 30,000ft; over 1,650mph (Mach 2.5) at 30,000ft) (projected development)
Climb rate	Over 50,000ft/minute at sea level
Tactical radius	500–1,500 miles, dependent upon speed, altitude and warload
Ferry range	3,300 miles (on internal fuel); 4,250 miles (with external tanks)
Warload (maximum)	6,000lb internal; 8,000lb external

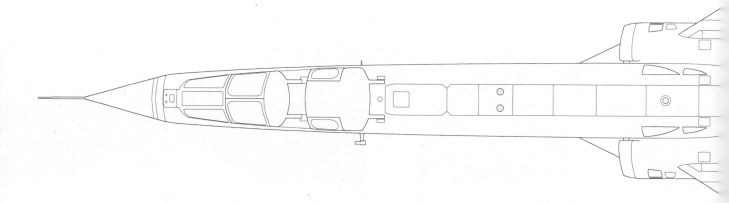

TSR.2 EXTERNAL FINISH

Airframe	High-Speed Acrylic White (ICI F153-R801) except for tailcone (polished metal), radome, undernose periscope sighting head and all antenna and other dielectric panels (natural finish).
National insignia	Upperwing roundels 60in overall, with 40in diameter white disc and 20in diameter red centre; fuselage roundels 36in overall, with 24in diameter white disc and 12in diameter red centre; colours similar to ICI 153-R802 (pale red) and ICI 153-R803 (pale blue). No underwing roundels. Fin flashes 24in square, colours as foregoing.
Serial numbers	Height 16in and thickness 2in in all four positions, in pale blue as above.
Other external markings	Pale red or pale blue as above. (As a generalisation, warning notices appeared in the former and information notices in the latter colour.)

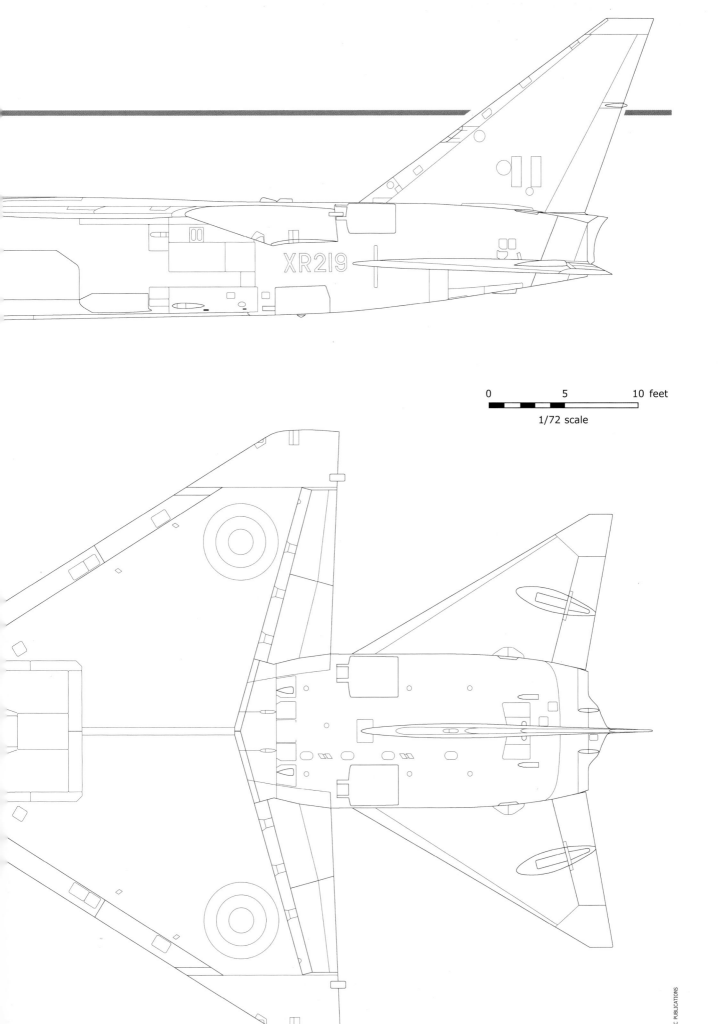

0   5   10 feet

1/72 scale

XR219

FIFTY-THREE

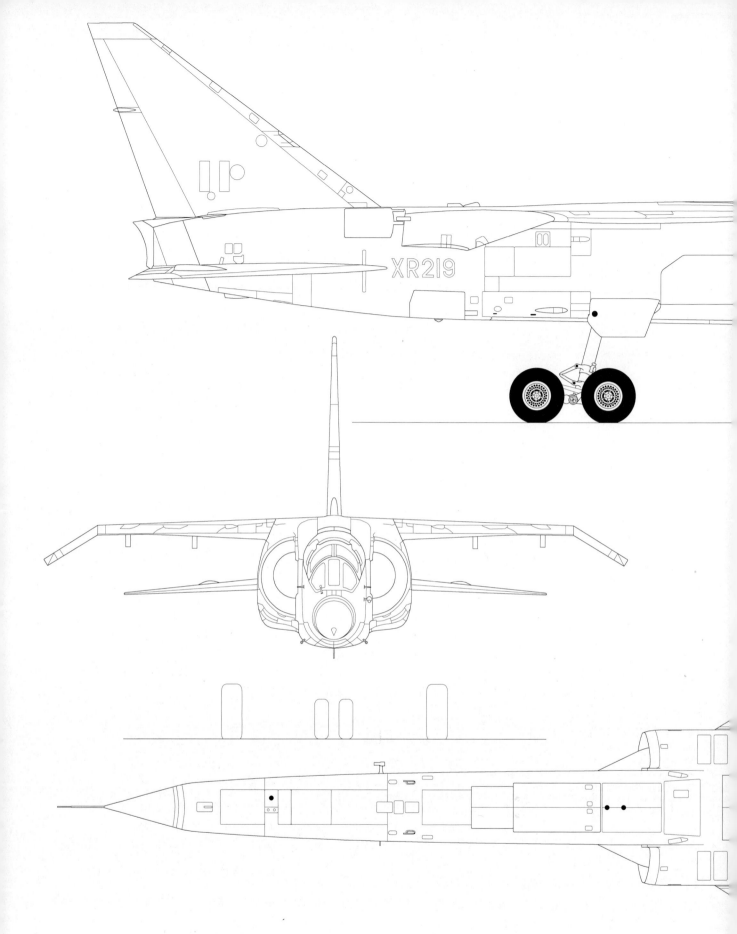

TSR.2 ALLOCATED SERIAL NUMBERS

Prototype aircraft (9)	XR219–XR227
Pre-production/trials aircraft (11)	XS660–XS670
Initial production aircraft (30)	XS994–XS954, XS977–XS995

0   5   10 feet

1/72 scale

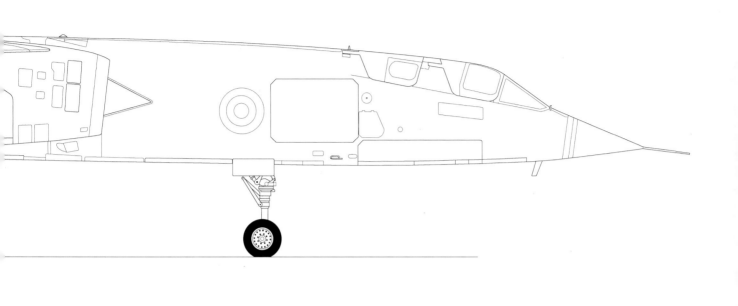

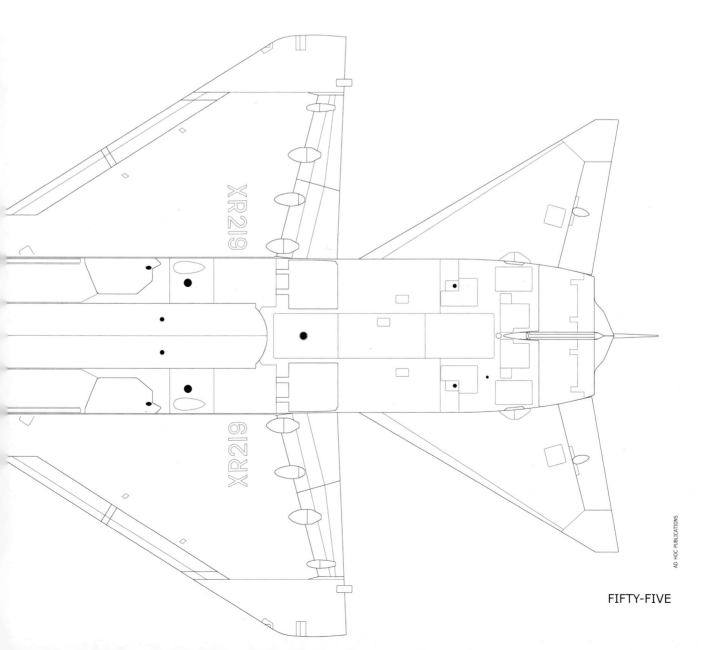

AD HOC PUBLICATIONS

FIFTY-FIVE

FINIS

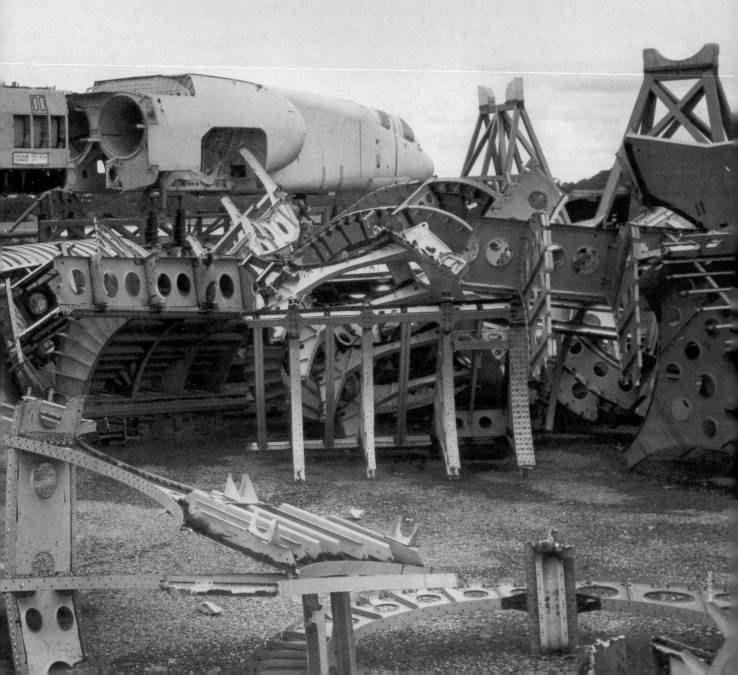